D1460716

A LIFEBUILDER BIBLE STUDY

EPHESIANS
Wholeness for a Broken World

*13 Studies
for individuals or groups*

Andrew T. & Phyllis J. Le Peau

SCRIPTURE UNION
207–209 Queensway, Bletchley, Milton Keynes, MK2 2EB

© 1985 by Inter-Varsity Christian Fellowship of the United States of America
First published in the United States by InterVarsity Press
First published in Great Britain by Scripture Union, 1986
Reprinted 1987, 1988, 1989, 1991, 1996

All rights reserved. No part of this publication may be reproduced, stored in a retrieval system, or transmitted, in any
form or by any means, electronic, mechanical, photocopying, recording or otherwise, without the prior permission of
Scripture Union.

All Scripture quotations, unless otherwise indicated, are taken from the Holy Bible, New International Version,
copyright © 1973, 1978, 1984 by International Bible Society, published by Hodder and Stoughton.

ISBN 0 86201 429 8

Cover photograph: Gary Irving

Printed in England by Ebenezer Baylis & Son Limited, The Trinity Press, Worcester, and London

Contents

Getting the Most
from LifeBuilder Bible Studies

Many of us long to fill our minds and our lives with Scripture. We desire to be transformed by its message. LifeBuilder Bible Studies are designed to be an exciting, thought-provoking and challenging way to do just that. Their ultimate goal is to help us build our lives on God's Word.

How They Work

LifeBuilder Bible Studies have a number of distinctive features. Perhaps the most important is that they are *inductive* rather than *deductive*. In other words, they lead us to *discover* what the Bible says rather than simply *telling* us what it says.

They are also thought provoking. They help us to think about the meaning of the passage so that we can truly understand what the author is saying. The questions require more than one-word answers.

The studies are personal. Questions expose us to the promises, assurances, exhortations and challenges of God's Word. They are designed to allow the Scriptures to renew our minds so that we can be transformed by the Spirit of God. This is the ultimate goal of all Bible study.

The studies are versatile. They are designed for student, neighborhood and church groups. They are also effective for individual study.

How They're Put Together

LifeBuilder Bible Studies also have a distinctive format. Each study need take no more than forty-five minutes in a group setting or thirty minutes in personal study—unless you choose to take more time.

The studies can be used within a quarter system in a church and fit well in a semester or trimester system on a college campus. If a guide has more than thirteen studies, it is divided into two or occasionally three parts of approximately twelve studies each.

LifeBuilder Bible Studies use a workbook format. Space is provided for writing answers to each question. This is ideal for personal study and allows group members to prepare in advance for the discussion.

The studies also contain leader's notes. They show how to lead a group discussion, provide additional background information on certain questions, give helpful tips on group dynamics and suggest ways to deal with problems which may arise during the discussion. With such helps, someone with little or no experience can lead an effective study.

Suggestions for Individual Study

1. As you begin each study, pray that God will help you to understand and apply the passage to your life.

2. Read and reread the assigned Bible passage to familiarize yourself with what the author is saying. In the case of book studies, you may want to read through the entire book prior to the first study. This will give you a helpful overview of its contents.

3. A good modern translation of the Bible, rather than the King James Version or a paraphrase, will give you the most help. The New International Version, the New American Standard Bible and the Revised Standard Version are all recommended. However, the questions in this guide are based on the New International Version.

4. Write your answers in the space provided in the study guide. This will help you to express your understanding of the passage clearly.

5. It might be good to have a Bible dictionary handy. Use it to look up any unfamiliar words, names or places.

Suggestions for Group Study

1. Come to the study prepared. Follow the suggestions for individual study mentioned above. You will find that careful preparation will greatly enrich your time spent in group discussion.

2. Be willing to participate in the discussion. The leader of your group will not be lecturing. Instead, he or she will be encouraging the members of the group to discuss what they have learned from the passage. The leader will be asking the questions that are found in this guide. Plan to share what God has taught you in your individual study.

3. Stick to the passage being studied. Your answers should be based on the verses which are the focus of the discussion and not on outside authorities such as commentaries or speakers. This guide deliberately avoids jumping from book to book or passage to passage. Each study focuses on only one passage. Book studies are generally designed to lead you through the book in the order in which it was written. This will help you follow the author's argument.

4. Be sensitive to the other members of the group. Listen attentively when they share what they have learned. You may be surprised by their insights! Link what you say to the comments of others so the group stays on the topic. Also, be affirming whenever you can. This will encourage some of the more hesitant members of the group to participate.

5. Be careful not to dominate the discussion. We are sometimes so eager to share what we have learned that we leave too little opportunity for others to respond. By all means participate! But allow others to also.

6. Expect God to teach you through the passage being discussed and through the other members of the group. Pray that you will have an enjoyable and profitable time together.

7. If you are the discussion leader, you will find additional suggestions and helpful ideas for each study in the leader's notes. These are found at the back of the guide.

Introducing Ephesians

Let's face it. Most of us are problem centered. How will I get all my work done on time? What can I do to be a better witness? Why isn't my ministry more effective?

Solving all these problems is good. But so often we lack a broader perspective. We put Band-Aids over gaping wounds instead of looking for long-term solutions. We lack vision so we fail to ask why we are involved in these activities at all.

I have enjoyed going back again and again to Paul's letter to the Ephesians because it communicates the Christian vision more powerfully and succinctly than any of his other letters. Most of Paul's other letters are directed to the particular problems of a given church. For example, he wrote to the Galatians about the threat of legalism. He addressed a variety of problems at the church at Corinth. But his letter to the Ephesians is blissfully free from turmoil.

Some believe the letter has this quality because it was not written solely for the church at Ephesus. Rather it was probably a circular letter sent to the Christian communities of Asia and other provinces, especially where Paul was not personally known. While most of his letters are full of personal greetings, no individuals are mentioned here or greeted by name. In fact the oldest and best manuscripts even lack the words *in Ephesus* (1:1). They are addressed generally "to the saints who are also faithful in Christ Jesus." But at an early date the letter became associated with the Ephesian church, so most later manuscripts have "to the saints in Ephesus, the faithful in Christ Jesus."

Ultimately, however, this letter is written to us, whoever the original readers were. It enables us to see the full sweep of God's program from before creation to the ultimate union of everyone and everything in Jesus Christ. It puts our problems and our entire lives in the context of eternity.

This guide offers you the opportunity to capture God's vision for all of history by studying Ephesians. It comes in the form of thirteen studies for individuals or groups. The first study helps you look over the entire letter to give a context for the following eleven studies. These each cover about half a chapter. But they are not isolated, independent discussions. They build on each other until the final study which reviews the entire book.

May Ephesians expand your vision of what God is doing in history and give you wholeness in this broken world.

1
A Letter from a Friend

Ephesians 1—6

Everyone likes getting mail. A letter from a friend is every bit as satisfying as a warm piece of pie fresh out of the oven. Paul's letter to the Ephesians may be unlike any letter you've ever gotten, but it is still a good word from a friend.

In this study we'll look over the whole letter to orient us to some of the basic issues that will come up in later studies. Most importantly, it will help us put those issues in the context of the whole book.

---

1. What thoughts and feelings do you have when you receive a letter from a close friend?

---

2. Read Ephesians 1—6. What are some of the main topics Paul covers in this letter? *riches & inheritence as children of god, new character, spiritual warfare. live on gods strenght attitudes to one another. new thing (promise of christ) was for everyone. enter into deeper relationship with god. unity*

3. Although virtually nothing is stated directly about the people Paul is writing to, what can you infer about them from the kinds of subjects he brings up? *for imature and mature, people with drink problems.*

4. What kind of person do you find Paul to be here?

in other letters he is very oppinunated / this letter Ephesians he is quite humble and passionate a father in the faith who has something to say.

5. What would you say is the basic tone of the letter—gruff, friendly, serious, melancholy or what? Explain.

passionate / prayer like

6. Into what main sections would you divide this book and why?

What four- to five-word title would you give to each section?

Christ is the centre. Renewal of personal life basically 2 sections 1st part gods purpose 2nd part how to practically play your part

7. What unifying theme, if any, do you see in this letter? Where do you see it?

His wholeness throughout.

8. What in the letter troubles you most, or what do you have the most difficulty understanding? Why?

without historical backgraund the Jews/Gentile situation was.
Jews did not regard Gentiles as worthy of anything

9. What do you find to be the most exciting or encouraging part of this letter? Why? *Power which raised christ from dead is in us.*
Armour of god.
Parent/Child relationship with our parents sometimes har to follow these thought paterns

Wife/husband. Instead of standing up for ourselves submit to god then your husband, because you will do what. Christ wants

2
The Purpose of God
Ephesians 1:1-14

We have a love-hate relationship with God's will. We dearly want to discover it and obey it, to be secure in knowing we are following the path he desires. On the other hand, we definitely don't want to find out what he wants because deep down we suspect it may not be to our liking. In this study we'll see what Paul says about God's will.

1. Complete the following statement. I feel God's will is: (a) a ball and chain around my neck, (b) a goal to reach, (c) reassuring, (d) unknowable, (e) something to rejoice in, (f) something to fear, (g) something to discover and then do. Explain your answer.

b or g.

2. Read Ephesians 1:1-14. According to verses 3-6, what blessings are ours from the Father?

his grace, love, every spiritual blessing to be his children
holy & blameless perfect in his eyes
he chose us.

What other blessings, according to verses 7-12, do we have in Jesus Christ? we are choosen by him
redemption through his blood,
forgiveness of sins
gods grace , wisdom & understanding
he made known his will to us.

3. Which of these is most significant to you? Explain.
I dont undersand gods grace & love but have to learn
to trust,
√11 We are his gifts and he delights in us,
√4 We are holy & blameless in his eyes'

4. Ephesians 1:1-14 uses words like *the will of God, chose, predestined, according to the plan* and *the purpose of his will.* Much emotion can surround the discussion of such words. What is Paul's emotional reaction to being chosen and predestined? confident & certain

an amazing free gift

What is yours?

its unbelievable

5. From the information given in 1:1-14 alone, try to formulate a clear statement of what it means to be chosen by God.

biggest honour on earth. √14

6. In the New Testament, the word *mystery* is not used of some murky idea we can never understand but of a secret which has now been revealed (see 3:4-5). According to 1:9-10, God has blessed us by revealing the ultimate goal of all history. What is it?

to bring all things from heaven & earth together. — unity

---

7. What would it mean to bring all things under Christ?

all people would be working in gods will

---

8. What blessings do we receive through the Holy Spirit (vv. 13-14)?

guarentee on our inheritence hallmarked.

---

9. Summarize God's redeeming purpose from eternity past to eternity future as described in 1:3-14.

to bring us into the fullness of his will for us

---

10. What motivated God to undertake this plan and give us all these blessings (vv. 5, 9)?

gods good pleasure. Gods love creates everything

praise is giving over our lives in singing

11. What does it mean to live "to the praise of his glory" (1:6, 12, 14)?

to always thank/praise god for his creation and presence.
accept what he has taught us.

How can we do this?

spend time with him as often as poss

---

12. How has this passage increased your sense of participation in God's total purpose of the universe? Explain. *accepting all he se* *I have never contemplated gods grace so mu* *I have never thought that it was gods pleas* *to pick us individually*

---

13. Spend time in praise to the God and Father of our Lord Jesus Christ who has blessed us with every spiritual blessing.

3
"I Keep Asking"
Ephesians 1:15-23

Sometimes prayer can be like pushing a full wheelbarrow—with no wheel. At other times it's like rushing down the rapids of a mountain river. What makes the difference? In this study we'll see why Paul's prayers overflow with praise and thanksgiving.

1. When you pray for fellow Christians, how do you usually pray for them? Give some specific examples. *gods will to be done in their lives, Blessings from god, strength, encouragement, Peace, joy, their relationship with god. Its very give me, give me, even if asking for someone else.*

2. Read Ephesians 1:15-23. In verses 15-16 Paul says, "For this reason . . . I have not stopped giving thanks for you, remembering you in my prayers." Why is Paul so thankful in his prayers for the Ephesians?

because they had faith in Jesus and believed in the Saints

Why do you suppose these things were so important to him?

because these two things are vital to being Christians
Encouragement to Paul, he had told them and they were acting correctly to the truth

3. How do Paul's prayers for his readers cover the past, the present and the future?

Past- given thanks for what they have done.
Present - What they are doing now. wisdom e
future - the eye of your hearts be enlightened

4. Why do you think Paul's prayers focus on wisdom, revelation and knowledge?

have these gifts so that we may know him
better.

5. Compare and contrast Paul's prayers with those you mentioned in answering the first question in this study.

I tend to ask god to solve the problems that
Christians are going through.
Paul is praying for gods will and eternity

6. How does Paul emphasize the tremendous power available "for us who believe" (1:19)?

gods incomparable great power for us who beli

7. How has this power been active in your life?

god uses us in every situation of life
being content with your life not longing
for more and more.

always being available for god and others

8. How does 1:20-23 expand on Paul's discussion of Christ's headship begun in 1:9-10?

enhanse what he said before,
expanding on Gods place.

9. How is the church, the body of believers, so central to God's plans for the universe?

the church has completed gods plan. We are
gods speakers, doing his work.

10. What role does the church play in your life?

big role. Becoming more important

11. How is Ephesians 1 itself an answer to the prayers Paul has been praying for his readers?

because they have and are doing everything
Paul has prayed for.

12. What kind of prayer dominates 1:3-14?

praise & thanksgiving

ALTAR

13. What kind of prayer dominates 1:15-23?

intersession · adaration, love, thanks,
Ask, Reverence.

14. How does intercession naturally flow out of praise?

praise opens you to god.
acknowledge. how great god is and our part
in his plan.

15. Spend several minutes praising God and then praying for Christ's church, or individuals in it, following Paul's example.

4
Amazing Grace

Ephesians 2:1-10

One of the best-known verses in the book of Ephesians is 2:8, "By grace you have been saved, through faith." *Grace* has often been defined by the acrostic, God's Riches At Christ's Expense. In this study we'll consider some of the riches we have been given in Christ.

1. How might your life be different if God ceased to be gracious?

forgiveness of god. he cant help but be nice

2. Read Ephesians 2:1-10. In verse 1 Paul says, "You were dead in your transgressions and sins." How does sin kill?

you die when you die instead of going to heaven

3. In verses 2-3 Paul mentions three negative influences on our lives which were later put into the formula of "the world, the flesh and the devil." According to Paul, how did each of these affect our lives as non-Christians?

We see things we want but it still not satisfied

4. How have you seen these influences at work?

Video . TV. Gossip .

5. According to verses 4-7, what motivated God to save us?

his love for us , mercy . grace . Kindness new life

Why are these motives so remarkable when you consider our condition as non-Christians?

We dont deserve it.

Greatest Commandment love each other as he loves us.

6. What parallels do you see between 2:4-6 and 1:19-20?

describe gods great power and how we have access to them.

7. What does Paul mean when he says we have been "made alive," "raised" and "seated" with Christ (vv. 5-6)?

made alive — made aware /eyes opened
raised — gods power that are available to
seated — our hope for the future.

How does our union with Christ relate to the fulfillment of God's purpose stated in 2:7 and 1:9-10? *set your minds on thin*

We have started a new life
seated with him we are no longer below him
we are on the same level

we are gods workers   if we know christ we are playing our in gods plan

8. What do we learn about God's grace from 2:4-10?

free and gift

9. When Paul says that our salvation is not from ourselves (vv. 8-9), is he saying that we play no role in our salvation? Explain.

We are saved through faith even faith is a gift, we have to accept

10. Does verse 10 contradict verses 8-9? Explain.

When we accept god then says now my spirit can work on you at no set rate. Gods spirit won't let you forget him

11. What good works has God prepared for you to do?

not the action its the feeling and motovation behind what you do.

12. What has hindered you from doing these?

13. Thank God specifically for some of the many ways he has been gracious to you. Ask him to remove the barriers to the good works he has created for you to do.

5
We Are One

Ephesians 2:11-22

Many of us have sung, "We are one in the Spirit; we are one in the Lord." But we also continue to find ourselves at odds with Christians who believe or live differently than we do. Such problems were just as common in Paul's day as in ours.

1. What groups of Christians do you disagree with or have trouble getting along with?

extremes - one way or another | Money seeking
conduct or code based christian / liberal Christians
gay marages

What causes these tensions?

they are wrong. not fare to push your oppinion

2. Read Ephesians 2:11-22. Paul uses vivid imagery in this passage. What are some of these images?

wall of hostility   building   holy temple
foundation   one body out of two   foreigners aliens
cornerstone.

What are they intended to communicate?

to make a picture seeing yourself a part of something much bigger than me going to church Very strong picture

---

3. How does verse 11 emphasize the ill feeling between the Jews and the Gentiles?

uncircumcised — unclean name calling

---

4. What name-calling do Christians engage in today—perhaps even using biblical terms?

happy clappies - god squad - bible bashers harry carries -

---

5. Besides some superficial differences between Jews and Gentiles, there were also some very real divisions. What are some of the things that divided Gentiles from Jews (v. 12)?

totally outlawed — God made promises to Jews only - anybody else. Executed if entered the temple

---

6. How does the bond we have in the blood (death) of Christ supersede all that divides us from other Christians (v. 13)?

belief in god means we hve salvation what christ has done is what united us

7. According to 2:14-18, what two reconciliations does Christ achieve?

*peace to your fellow man then brought
man to man — God to man. peace to (*

How are they related?

*if you are not at one with fellow christians
you are not in the best relationship with
God the two relationships are tied togethe*

---

8. There was a literal "dividing wall of hostility" (2:14) in Jerusalem. The Court of the Gentiles was separated from the Temple proper by a stone wall. This wall had a sign on it forbidding entrance to any foreigner on pain of death. Paul says Christ destroyed this barrier "by abolishing in his flesh the law with its commandments and regulations" (2:15). In what sense did the cross abolish the law?

*brought them together buy dying he was
now the sacrafice instead of priest offering
Sacrafice for people.*

What rules and requirements do we enforce which might hinder people from coming into the kingdom?

---

9. We still see divisions among Christians today even though Christ himself is our peace (vv. 14-18). How can those who are united in Christ still be divided?

*we owe it to Christ to say it doesnt matter
what we dont agree on lets talk about what we
do agree on.
lack of love and understanding that makes
us divide*

10. How do the images Paul uses in 2:19-22 emphasize the unity Christians have with one another?

interdependant — all denominations have a place - if one brick is removed the lot could fall.

---

11. How is the reconciliation of Jews and Gentiles to each other and to God (2:11-22) one fulfillment of God's will and purpose in Christ (1:9-10)?

to bring all things on heaven and earth together

---

12. What practical first step toward unity can you take in the next week with Christians you differ with?

see the thing that unite rather than our differences

6
Prisoner and Preacher

Ephesians 3:1-21

W hat do you think of when you hear the word *church*? A building on the corner? A stuffy group of religious hypocrites? A vibrant fellowship? Paul's special ministry enables him to enlarge our conception of the church. In this passage he clarifies and exalts its place in God's plan.

---

1. Think of two or three adjectives which summarize your attitude and experience of the church. Explain.

livley, illuminating, joyfull, tiring, turgid (full entertaining enriching *bu*

---

2. Read Ephesians 3:1-21. What gifts of God's grace does Paul say he has received (vv. 2-3, 8)?

revelation of the mystery of god.
the riches of god.

---

3. Explain the meaning of the mystery revealed to Paul (vv. 2-6).

that Jews and gentiles would all be saved

How is it connected with the ministry given to him (vv. 7-13)?

it is his ministry to preach what god has revealed to him

4. What purpose does God have for the church (vv. 10-11)?

through the church learn his wisdom exactly according to his will

5. How does this mesh with God's overall purpose in Christ described in 1:9-10?

already covered this

6. Paul was in prison "for the sake of you Gentiles" (v. 1). The Jews who arrested him reacted against the kind of teaching Paul has just expressed in Ephesians 2. Namely, Jesus has abolished the divisive elements of the law and is creating a *new* people and building a *new* temple. How then was Paul's imprisonment to the glory of his readers (3:13)?

through his imprisonment he wrote all these letters which formed bible his suffering is for our glory.

7. Paul now turns from instruction to prayer. What was the reason for Paul's prayer for his readers (vv. 1, 14)?

he wanted them to be really struck by what he was experiencing and writing he hoped they would get down and pray.

8. Three times in verses 14-21 Paul mentions "love" and "power." What do we learn about power and love in these verses?

power for living — roots that will hold us in the storm.

9. Verses 10-11 state that the church is to make known God's wisdom. How is Paul's prayer directed toward fulfilling that purpose?

through the knowledge of gods love. We would change to be more like Jes gods rulers and authorities in heaven will see a unity as a church being gods manifold wi

10. How is God's wisdom being made known through your local body of believers?

our unity in Catterline is that we all hav come from different backgrounds and diff experiences and we are a strengthe group

11. To what extent has his prayer been answered in your life or in the life of your church?

through his love he has brought us together, and kept us together reveal more of himself to us

12. How does the benediction of 3:20-21 tie together the main themes that have run through the first three chapters of Ephesians?

all in 1-3 is more than we would imagin and he has done it

13. Choose at least one item from Paul's prayer and make it a prayer of your own, for yourself and your church.

7
Unity and Uniqueness
Ephesians 4:1-16

W hile Ephesians 1—3 provides a doctrinal foundation, Ephesians 4—6 shows in practical detail how to give glory to God in the church. Paul now considers the quality of life that is demanded of believers individually and in the fellowship of Christ's church.

---

1. "To have unity we must all be uniform." Explain why you do or do not agree with this statement.

---

2. Read Ephesians 4:1-16. Paul is so concerned for these Christians that he *begs* them to lead a life worthy of their calling. According to Ephesians 1—3, what is the calling to which they have been called?

1v5 Called to be sons & daughters
1v12 Give glory to god
2v10 do good works

3. What are the characteristics of a life which is worthy of our calling (vv. 1-3)?

4. Why are these virtues so important for maintaining unity?

being humble.

5. Which qualities help you foster unity with others? Which do you still need to work on?

6. We are commanded to keep the unity of the Spirit. But Paul also says we already have one body, one Spirit, one hope, one Lord, one faith, one baptism and one God and Father of all. If we are already one, then why must Paul also command us to be one?

like being married - you are one but takes effort to remain one.

How do these seven "ones" contribute to actually living out true unity?

terms relate to all our different facets.

7. In verses 8-10 Christ is compared to a conquering hero whose triumphal procession fills "the whole universe," from the highest heaven to the lowest earth. He then generously distributes gifts (the spoils of victory) to his loyal followers. What is the nature and purpose of these gifts (vv. 11-13)?

for the works of service

8. What spiritual gifts do you think you might have?

9. How do they fulfill the purposes described in 4:11-13?

10. How does spiritual infancy differ from spiritual maturity (vv. 14-16)?

that we are not diswayed by the waves of life but know what the truth is

11. What winds and waves are blowing and tossing the church today?

homosexual marrage be accepted -
abortion
divorce.
sexual immorality

12. While 4:1-6 sets forth the unity we have as believers, 4:7-11 describes our uniqueness through the individual gifts we have received. How does Paul's explanation of the proper function and goal of these gifts bring us right back to the opening theme of Ephesians 4?

we are to become mature christians
grow in Christ

13. In verse 16 Paul says that the body "grows and builds itself up in love, as each part does its work." What steps do you need to take to more fully work toward this goal?

8
Something Old, Something New
Ephesians 4:17-32

I t's easier said than done" is a cliché that certainly applies to Christian unity. Remnants of the "old self" (v. 22) too often get in the way. Somehow we manage to say the wrong thing or act the wrong way. Paul's aim in this passage is to help make Christian unity a little more "done."

---

1. Do Christians necessarily live better lives than non-Christians? Explain.

hopefully. depends who makes the standard. God is more concerned with peoples hearts than their works.

---

2. Read Ephesians 4:17-32. Paul continues to flesh out what it means for his readers to live a life worthy of their calling (4:1). How does he contrast the life of the Gentile (unbeliever) with that of a true believer?

ainting a very black & white picture is christians we have a glimse of gods perspective

---

3. Paul says the Gentiles are afflicted with a spiritual condition known as hardness of heart (4:18). Explain the meaning of his diagnosis.

they have shut their hearts to gods words.

What are the effects of this condition (vv. 17-19)?

they do not know what is right and wrong therefore continue their way not gods.

4. How have you struggled with hardness of heart?

hardness of heart mine is to protect myself

5. What does it mean to put off the old self (4:22)?

stop doing what you know to be wrong

6. How do your attitudes affect the way you live (4:23)?

7. In verses 25-32 what does Paul tell us to put off, what does he say to put on and what reason does he give for doing these things? (If he doesn't explicitly state each of the three parts for a given topic, fill in what is implied.)

stop lying tell the truth because we are members of one family

8. How do these instructions show the importance of healthy communication in promoting unity?

you have to communicate to build each other up instead of breaking each other, forgive too.

9. Which of the commands in verses 25-32 do you have the most difficulty following? Explain.

choice with truth to neighbour. sinning in Anger giving the devil a foothole. unwholesome talk forgive others as god forgave us.

10. What practical steps could you take this week to improve your relationships with others in this area of difficulty?

recognise your triggers ask god to defuse the situation (Like Josh saying Jesus) when in trouble. submit to husband with reverence to Christ

11. Which of the commands in verses 25-32 have you seen God strengthen you to obey?

trying to witness about God. Sinning in Anger. really god has changed me in all the things above — but still has a lot of work to do!

12. Spend time praising God for his work in your life, and pray that he will give you grace in the areas needing improvement.

9
Live in Love, Live in Light

Ephesians 5:1-21

Not doing what is wrong is one thing. But sometimes it can be even more difficult to do what is right. In Ephesians 5 Paul continues to outline what it means "to live a life worthy of the calling you have received" (4:1). He does this by considering ways we shouldn't act and ways we should.

1. How do children imitate? (Give some examples from your own observations of small children.)

2. Read Ephesians 5:1-21. In verses 1-2 Paul says that just as children imitate their parents, so we are to imitate God. What have you observed about God which you have begun or could begin to imitate?

3. How is Christ the perfect example of what Paul asks of us (v. 2)?

4. How is thanksgiving an appropriate replacement for the behavior Paul condemns in 5:3-4?

How can you use thanksgiving to replace improper behavior in your life?

---

5. Why will immoral, impure or greedy people be unable to inherit the kingdom (vv. 5-7)?

---

6. Why are such people considered idolaters?

---

7. In verses 8-14 Paul contrasts light and darkness to say more about holy living. According to these verses, what does it mean to "live as children of light"?

---

8. Often we equate wisdom with intelligence. What characterizes wise people according to 5:15-17?

9. How can you live more wisely then?

10. Verses 19-21 look like four separate commands in English. In Greek, however, they are actually linked grammatically to verse 18 and describe several beneficial results of being filled with the Spirit. In your own words, explain the characteristics of those who are filled with the Spirit.

11. Do these results occur automatically when we are filled with the Spirit or must we also treat them as commands to be followed? Explain.

12. According to Paul's definition of filling, in what area do you most need to be filled with the Spirit?

13. Spend time singing and making music in your heart to the Lord, or (if in a group) speaking or singing to one another with psalms, hymns and spiritual songs.

10
Wives and Husbands
Ephesians 5:21-33

A lot of emotion and misunderstanding surrounds the word *submit*. So try to come to this text as if you had never seen it before. Try to set aside your own biases and see what Paul really has to say on the subject of submission.

1. How do you react to the idea of being told to submit to someone?

Depends who you are being asked to submit to.

2. Read Ephesians 5:21-33. How does verse 21 preview this passage?

the picture is what you are doing for god, not how you feel about who you are submitting to.

3. Paul says wives are to submit to their husbands as to the Lord (v. 22). What does it mean to submit to the Lord?

To do gods will

attitude in which you do it

defer to gods judgement even if you would rather do something else

4. Why is the church's submission to the Lord a helpful illustration of a wife's submission to her husband?

Heb 12 v 2 · bad comparosum – the church

5. If you are a wife, how could your submission to your husband grow more like your submission to Christ? running of household and children (do things only in certain circumstan for husband) for God instead of What does he need just now think how does he want something done.

If you are a single woman, how can you grow in your submission to Christ?

6. Does submission mean putting your mind in neutral? Explain.

no · — but go to god.

7. In verse 25 Paul instructs husbands to love their wives as Christ loved the church. How has Christ shown his love for the church?

by laying down his life for it

8. The word *love* in 5:25 and 28 is used to translate the Greek word *agapaō*, meaning totally unselfish, sacrificial love. How are husbands to show love for their wives (vv. 25-30)?

9. If you are a husband, how could your love for your wife grow more like Christ's love for the church?

10. In verse 31 Paul quotes Genesis 2:24 to root his arguments about the unity of husband and wife in creation itself. How do verses 31-33 summarize his teaching on the unity that is to exist between wives and husbands?

1) the pecking order is set in beginning
Christ left his parents to become one with
the church as in marraige

11. Why do you think Paul calls on wives to *respect* their husbands while he calls on husbands to *love* their wives (v. 33)?

because men and women need different
things

12. If you are a woman, how could you show respect to your husband? If you are a man, how could you show love to your wife?

take infirmaties more seriously
dont argue in public
do thing in the right attitude

11
Children, Parents, Slaves, Masters

Ephesians 6:1-9

How much our parents mean to us—yet how difficult they can be! How much we love our children—yet how exasperating they are at times! In nine packed verses Paul not only delves into these important relationships but those of the work world as well.

1. How would you characterize the relationship you have had with your parents?

difficult - sensitive
try to gain their acceptance

2. Read Ephesians 6:1-9. How does this passage continue the theme of mutual submission begun in 5:21?

that all relationships submis
to god comes first to put all ot
in place

3. What reasons are given for obeying and honoring parents (vv. 1-3)? *1st commandment (great in*
christian families)

Explain your understanding of the promise given to those who honor their parents.

4. Is it possible to obey your parents without honoring them? Explain.

Yes you can obey and not agree to what they want done, as long as its acceptable to god.

5. What are some practical ways you can obey or honor your parents?

) looking after them in old age.
) byte your tounge instead of winding them up
phone regularly.

6. How can fathers (and mothers) exasperate their children (6:4)?

expecting too much from them
setting too high a standard
different standards from kids & adults.

7. Why does Paul contrast exasperating children with bringing "them up in the training and instruction of the Lord" (6:4)?

if you bring your kids up knowing the Lord, and show them by example they will know what is right

8. John Stott writes, "The instruction to children to obey their parents presupposes . . . parental authority. Yet when Paul outlines how parents should behave towards their children, it is not the exercise, but the restraint, of their authority which he urges upon them."[1] If you are a parent, what can you do this week to follow verse 4 more closely? (If you are not a parent, how have you seen verse 4 in action?)

we have the authority but not to abuse it
spend more time teaching them about god
showing them how much they mean to you

9. What is implied about the way slaves normally worked for their masters (vv. 5-8)?

they are shirkers and
unwilling

10. How and why were Christian slaves to be different?

they were to be keen in everything
they were asked to do.
have the right attitudes

11. How could the principles Paul considers in 6:5-8 be lived out in situations you have been in or are in?

have the right attitudes to people
great gift to be able to encourage.
2 ways of getting things done through fear or
cooperation

[1]John Stott, *The Message of Ephesians* (Downers Grove, Ill.: InterVarsity Press, 1979), p. 245.

12. Paul says masters should treat slaves the way he wants slaves to treat masters because both have the same Master in heaven. Why should this make a difference in how slaves are treated?

mutual respect.

13. What implications does this have for how employers treat employees?

encouragement, honesty be fair.
consistant· gain respect of employees

14. How does 6:1-9 contribute to the theme of the church glorifying God through visible unity?

keeping Relationships in gods will
one head of church — christ
all be willing servants

12
Prayer
Wars

Ephesians 6:10-24

In a war of bullets, careful aim and heavy armor win battles. In a war of words, eloquent speech and sharp pens overcome the opposition. But if the fight is outside the realm of sight, sound and touch, how are victories won?

1. How do you respond to the idea that there are spiritual forces in the universe that are working against God's will?

2. Read Ephesians 6:10-24. In 6:10-12 Paul emphasizes that our struggle is not with flesh and blood. How has he emphasized this same point elsewhere in his letter?

3. How do you sense a battle around you with more than physical forces and foes?

4. Four times in verses 11-14 Paul urges his readers to stand firm in the battle against the devil's stratagems. How are we susceptible to instability as Christians?

5. When Paul wrote Ephesians, he may have been chained to a Roman soldier (see 6:20). This could easily have inspired his analogy of 6:13-17. How does the "armor of God" prepare us for spiritual battle?

6. Which piece of armor do you need most to fight your spiritual battles? Explain.

7. In 6:10-12 Paul identifies our ally and enemies in battle. In 6:13-17 he considers our preparation and tactics. Now, how is the battle itself fought? Explain your answer.

8. In 6:18-20 Paul urges all kinds of prayers. How has he been a model of a prayer warrior throughout this letter?

9. What main obstacle do you face in fighting the battle of prayer more effectively?

10. Take time now to pray about your fight in spiritual warfare.

13
Looking Over the Letter Again
Ephesians 1—6

At the end of a journey we can look back with satisfaction at having reached our destination and at having learned much along the way. We may also have painful memories, however, of problems or obstacles we had to overcome. But whether the trip was easy or difficult, we are different for having made the trek. Likewise with Paul's letter to the Ephesians, whether our study was easy or difficult, we are different now. This last study offers an opportunity to reflect on the major themes of the book and on how we have changed (and will change) because of it.

1. Look throughout the letter for the words "in Christ" or "in him" (referring to Christ). From these passages, what do you learn about being "in Christ"?

2. How do you feel about being in union with Christ in so many ways?

3. Often in this study we have referred to 1:9-10. How has your vision of God's plans and purposes for the universe been expanded through Ephesians?

4. Ephesians 1:22-23 and 3:10-11 focus on the theme of the church which is implicit throughout the rest of the letter. How has your view of the church been altered through your study?

5. What is the most important thing you have learned about the unity of the body of Christ in this letter? Explain.

6. What steps are you taking to strengthen your oneness with other Christians?

7. While Paul focuses on the spiritual forces in the universe most obviously in 6:10-18, he has also referred to the heavenly places and spiritual forces of evil in 1:3, 20; 2:2, 6; and 3:10. How has your awareness of spiritual realms been expanded through Paul's letter?

8. What step might you take to stand more firmly against your spiritual opponents?

9. How do the first three chapters of Ephesians lay a foundation for the practical instructions of the last three?

10. What does 6:21-24 reveal about Paul?

11. How are the words *grace* and *peace,* which lead off verses 23-24, a fitting conclusion to Paul's letter?

12. What have you enjoyed most about your study of Ephesians?

Leader's Notes

Leading a Bible discussion can be an enjoyable and rewarding experience. But it can also be *scary*—especially if you've never done it before. If this is your feeling, you're in good company. When God asked Moses to lead the Israelites out of Egypt, he replied, "O Lord, please send someone else to do it!" (Ex 4:13).

When Solomon became king of Israel, he felt the task was far beyond his abilities. "I am only a little child and do not know how to carry out my duties. . . . Who is able to govern this great people of yours?" (1 Kings 3:7, 9).

When God called Jeremiah to be a prophet, he replied, "Ah, Sovereign LORD, . . . I do not know how to speak; I am only a child" (Jer 1:6).

The list goes on. The apostles were "unschooled, ordinary men" (Acts 4:13). Timothy was young, frail and frightened. Paul's "thorn in the flesh" made him feel weak. But God's response to all of his servants—including you—is essentially the same: "My grace is sufficient for you" (2 Cor 12:9). Relax. God helped these people in spite of their weaknesses, and he can help you in spite of your feelings of inadequacy.

There is another reason why you should feel encouraged. Leading a Bible discussion is not difficult if you follow certain guidelines. You don't need to be an expert on the Bible or a trained teacher. The suggestions listed below should enable you to effectively and enjoyably fulfill your role as leader.

Preparing to Lead

1. Ask God to help you understand and apply the passage to your own life. Unless this happens, you will not be prepared to lead others. Pray too for the various members of the group. Ask God to give you an enjoyable and profitable time together studying his Word.

2. As you begin each study, read and reread the assigned Bible passage to familiarize yourself with what the author is saying. In the case of book studies, you may want to read through the entire book prior to the first study. This will give you a helpful overview of its contents.

3. This study guide is based on the New International Version of the Bible. It will help you and the group if you use this translation as the basis for your study and discussion. Encourage others to use the NIV also, but allow them the freedom to use whatever translation they prefer.

4. Carefully work through each question in the study. Spend time in meditation and reflection as you formulate your answers.

5. Write your answers in the space provided in the study guide. This will help you to express your understanding of the passage clearly.

6. It might help you to have a Bible dictionary handy. Use it to look up any unfamiliar words, names or places. (For additional help on how to study a passage, see chapter five of *Leading Bible Discussions*, IVP.)

7. Once you have finished your own study of the passage, familiarize yourself with the leader's notes for the study you are leading. These are designed to help you in several ways. First, they tell you the purpose the study guide author had in mind while writing the study. Take time to think through how the study questions work together to accomplish that purpose. Second, the notes provide you with additional background information or comments on some of the questions. This information can be useful if people have difficulty understanding or answering a question. Third, the leader's notes can alert you to potential problems you may encounter during the study.

8. If you wish to remind yourself of anything mentioned in the leader's notes, make a note to yourself below that question in the study.

Leading the Study

1. Begin the study on time. Unless you are leading an evangelistic Bible study, open with prayer, asking God to help you to understand and apply the passage.

2. Be sure that everyone in your group has a study guide. Encourage them to prepare beforehand for each discussion by working through the questions in the guide.

3. At the beginning of your first time together, explain that these studies are meant to be discussions not lectures. Encourage the members of the group to participate. However, do not put pressure on those who may be hesitant to speak during the first few sessions.

4. Read the introductory paragraph at the beginning of the discussion. This will orient the group to the passage being studied.

5. Read the passage aloud if you are studying one chapter or less. You may choose to do this yourself, or someone else may read if he or she has been asked to do so prior to the study. Longer passages may occasionally be read in parts at different times during the study. Some studies may cover several chapters. In such cases reading aloud would probably take too much time, so the group members should simply read the assigned passages prior to the study.

6. As you begin to ask the questions in the guide, keep several things in mind. First, the questions are designed to be used just as they are written. If you wish, you may simply read them aloud to the group. Or you may prefer to express them in your own words. However, unnecessary rewording of the questions is not recommended.

Second, the questions are intended to guide the group toward understanding and applying the *main idea* of the passage. The author of the guide has stated his or her view of this central idea in the *purpose* of the study in the leader's notes. You should try to understand how the passage expresses this idea and how the study questions work together to lead the group in that direction.

There may be times when it is appropriate to deviate from the study guide. For example, a question may have already been answered. If so, move on to the next question. Or someone may raise an important question not covered in the guide. Take time to discuss it! The important thing is to use discretion. There may be many routes you can travel to reach the goal of the study. But the easiest route is usually the one the author has suggested.

7. Avoid answering your own questions. If necessary, repeat or rephrase them until they are clearly understood. An eager group quickly becomes passive and silent if they think the leader will do most of the talking.

8. Don't be afraid of silence. People may need time to think about the question before formulating their answers.

9. Don't be content with just one answer. Ask, "What do the rest of you think?" or "Anything else?" until several people have given answers to the question.

10. Acknowledge all contributions. Try to be affirming whenever possible. Never reject an answer. If it is clearly wrong, ask, "Which verse led you to that conclusion?" or again, "What do the rest of you think?"

11. Don't expect every answer to be addressed to you, even though this will probably happen at first. As group members become more at ease, they will begin to truly interact with each other. This is one sign of a healthy discussion.

12. Don't be afraid of controversy. It can be very stimulating. If you don't resolve an issue completely, don't be frustrated. Move on and keep it in mind for later. A subsequent study may solve the problem.

   13. Stick to the passage under consideration. It should be the source for answering the questions. Discourage the group from unnecessary cross-referencing. Likewise, stick to the subject and avoid going off on tangents.

   14. Periodically summarize what the *group* has said about the passage. This helps to draw together the various ideas mentioned and gives continuity to the study. But don't preach.

   15. Conclude your time together with conversational prayer. Be sure to ask God's help to apply those things which you learned in the study.

   16. End on time.

   Many more suggestions and helps are found in *Leading Bible Discussions* (IVP). Reading and studying through that would be well worth your time.

Components of Small Groups

A healthy small group should do more than study the Bible. There are four components you should consider as you structure your time together.

   Nurture. Being a part of a small group should be a nurturing and edifying experience. You should grow in your knowledge and love of God and each other. If we are to properly love God, we must know and keep his commandments (Jn 14:15). That is why Bible study should be a foundational part of your small group. But you can be nurtured by other things as well. You can memorize Scripture, read and discuss a book, or occasionally listen to a tape of a good speaker.

   Community. Most people have a need for close friendships. Your small group can be an excellent place to cultivate such relationships. Allow time for informal interaction before and after the study. Have a time of sharing during the meeting. Do fun things together as a group, such as a potluck supper or a picnic. Have someone bring refreshments to the meeting. Be creative!

   Worship. A portion of your time together can be spent in worship and prayer. Praise God together for who he is. Thank him for what he has done and is doing in your lives and in the world. Pray for each other's needs. Ask God to help you to apply what you have learned. Sing hymns together.

   Mission. Many small groups decide to work together in some form of outreach. This can be a practical way of applying what you have learned. You can host a series of evangelistic discussions for your friends or neighbors. You can visit people at a home for the elderly. Help a widow with cleaning or repair jobs around her home. Such projects can have a transforming influence on your group.

   For a detailed discussion of the nature and function of small groups, read

Small Group Leaders' Handbook or *Good Things Come in Small Groups* (both from IVP).

Study 1. A Letter from a Friend. Ephesians 1—6.

Purpose: To gain an overview of the main aspects of Paul's letter to the Ephesians.

As the leader, you need to work through the study before consulting the leader's notes. You have to deal with the passage personally to lead the group as effectively as possible. So if you have not yet done study one, do so now. Then come back here.

Finished? Great. Let's hit some practical matters first.

Begin the study by taking five minutes to explain that the group will be learning by discussion, by each person's contribution which will be stimulated by a few thought-provoking questions. Review the "Suggestions for Group Study" (p. 6).

Question 1. Almost every study begins with an "approach" question, which is meant to be asked *before* the passage is read. These questions are important for several reasons. First, they help the group to warm up to each other. No matter how well a group may know each other or how comfortable they may be with each other, there is always a stiffness that needs to be overcome before people will begin to talk openly. A good question will break the ice.

Second, approach questions get people thinking along the lines of the topic of the study. Most people will have lots of different things going on in their minds (dinner, an important meeting coming up, how to get the car fixed) that will have nothing to do with the study. A creative question will get their attention and draw them into the discussion.

Third, approach questions can reveal where our thoughts or feelings need to be transformed by Scripture. This is why it is especially important *not* to read the passage before the approach question is asked. The passage will tend to color the honest reactions people would otherwise give because they are of course *supposed* to think the way the Bible does. Giving honest responses to various issues before they find out what the Bible says may help them to see where their thoughts or attitudes need to be changed.

After you have finished discussing the approach question, take five more minutes to summarize the key points from the introduction about Paul and the letter to the Ephesians, how it was probably circulated and why it has the characteristics it does. It is necessary that this type of information be in the hands of the group members so they will have an adequate background to answer questions 2 and 3. Even if the group has read the introduction and worked through study one beforehand, a quick review would help.

Question 2. There are three ways you can read Ephesians as a group. First, you could read the entire letter aloud. This could be done by one person, though we recommend several people take, for example, one chapter each. This will help avoid the possible monotony or difficulty of one person reading the whole book. It will also get several people involved in the reading so attention does not lapse. It will take about twenty minutes to read the whole book in this way.

Second, everyone could read the letter silently. You need to allow about fifteen minutes for this.

Third, if you are sure everyone in the group has read the letter already, you could take five minutes for each person to scan it. But be sure to use the first or second option if someone has not read it. Otherwise that person will be lost during the discussion.

Encourage several brief answers to this question. But give people time to flip back and forth in a quick search for main ideas.

Question 3. As mentioned in the introduction, because this letter was likely going to several churches and not just to the one at Ephesus, Paul avoids direct references to individuals or to particular problems in the congregation. But we can still gather some key information on his audience—their racial mix, their Christian background, the kinds of issues they faced and so on. Ask for this information from the group.

Questions 6-7. Realize that there may be many possible ways to answer these questions. Their purpose is to stimulate discussion and get people to struggle with the basic issues of the letter. Hopefully, answers will become more clear in subsequent studies. So by all means, don't answer the questions for the group. Just move on if discussion gets bogged down.

Question 8. Some might mention problems in dealing with anger or submission or honoring parents. Don't try to solve the problems mentioned as a result of this question. Its purpose is to allow people to express what's on their minds. It will also give you, the leader, an idea of what issues the group will need to grapple with while the studies progress. So mention at the end of the discussion that you hope the group will address these issues in the coming studies.

Study 2. The Purpose of God. Ephesians 1:1-14.

Purpose: To consider God's plan and purpose for all of history and all of creation, and the blessings he has given us as part of that plan.

Question 2. This is an observation question asking for specific privileges and benefits that belong to us in Christ.

Question 4. While praise is not merely emotional, it seems clear from the vigor of this passage that Paul has a very profound emotional response. This could be an important emphasis for people who tend to intellectualize their faith or equate it with a mere series of propositional truths.

Question 5. Try not to let the discussion deteriorate into a bull session on predestination versus free will. Rather, focus on what the passage says. What does it mean to be chosen? For example, Ephesians says that predestination affects our status in Christ. It does not say that every facet of our every action is controlled and foreordained by God.

Verses 11-14 also show that predestination does not necessarily limit the scope or availability of salvation. "In him we [the Jews] were also chosen . . . . And you [the Gentiles] also were included in Christ."

Adoption was a Roman custom (not a Jewish one) which emphasizes that our status is solely due to the will of the adopter and not to any right we have inherited by birth. Very early in his letter Paul indicates the equality of Jews and Gentiles in the kingdom.

Question 7. Verse 10 should not be mistaken as supporting universalism— the belief that all will be saved. Rather, it teaches that Christ will reign over all of creation.

Question 11. The glory of God is evident when God is revealed or made known. To live to the praise of his glory is thus to live and worship God in words and deeds. It is also to lead others to know him better and to praise him. Thus worship and evangelism are linked very closely, as are worship and study.

Study 3. "I Keep Asking." Ephesians 1:15-23.
Purpose: To view the model of prayer Paul offers us as he intercedes for the church.

Question 4. Don't get hung up on differences among wisdom, revelation and knowledge. They are essentially equivalent terms used to describe the enlightenment God gives.

Question 8. Some scholars have felt that 1:23 indicates that the church makes Christ complete. But the reverse is the more natural interpretation and is more consistent with the rest of the letter (e.g., 4:9-16). Christ makes the church a complete expression of his power, position and person. The church is central to Christ's headship of all creation.

Question 11. If the group is stumped by this one, try rephrasing it, such as, "How is the content of Ephesians 1:1-14 tied to the prayers of 1:15-23?"

Questions 12-14. These three questions go together. One-word answers are adequate for the first two. But it may take a minute for the group to respond to question 14 since it involves a review of the last study.

Study 4. Amazing Grace. Ephesians 2:1-10.

Purpose: To see how God has brought us from death to life by the riches of his grace.

Question 7. Ephesians 2:5-6 refers to Christ being "made alive," "raised" and "seated." The Apostles Creed formulated it this way: "The third day he rose again. He ascended into heaven, and is seated at the right hand of the Father." But what is so remarkable in Ephesians is that Paul is not just writing about Christ but about us as well. We now share a union with Christ who rules in the heavenly places.

By now the group should be starting to catch on that Ephesians 1:9-10 is the nub of the whole letter. God is bringing everything in the universe under Christ, and out of his love and mercy he has graciously chosen to begin with us, his people, as a sign of the complete fulfillment of his purpose which is yet to come.

Question 9. We receive "the gift of God" through faith. Thus we are actively involved as God saves us.

Question 10. This is not an easy question. Can good works be an important and necessary part of our lives without being the basis for our salvation? Allow discussion to flow freely, but bring the group's attention back to the passage as needed.

Study 5. We Are One. Ephesians 2:11-22.

Purpose: To see that Christ's death not only reconciled us to God but also to each other, and to consider the implications of this.

Question 1. Encourage the group to mention Christians they disagree with over doctrine or practice—even if it is a "friendly" disagreement. Charismatic versus noncharismatic, reformed versus dispensational, White versus Black, Catholic versus Protestant, Moral Majority versus Christian pacifists might be some of the conflicts mentioned. There might be others as well that are closer to the concerns of your group.

Question 2. The whole letter is incredibly rich in imagery and metaphorical language. In this passage especially, Paul can hardly get an idea out without using some kind of analogy to geographic distance, physical structures, new people, peace treaties and the like. If you want the group to understand Paul, you have to understand his imagery.

Question 8. The issue, of course, is, What is the essential gospel? What minimal requirements, if any, are there before we can say someone is in fellowship with us? Are we guilty of creating artificial barriers to God like some Jewish Christians who required gentile Christians to be circumcised? Ask the group to be honest. Almost all of us have some notions of what it means to be a "real" Christian based on extrabiblical requirements.

Study 6. Prisoner and Preacher. Ephesians 3:1-21.
Purpose: To look at the purpose of the church and its role in fulfilling God's plan.
Question 3. Regarding *mystery,* see the comment in study two, question 6. See also Ephesians 3:5.
Question 4. The "rulers" in 3:10 are probably spiritual beings.
Question 9. A pun is at work in the original Greek in 3:14-15 since "Father" is *pater* and "family" is *patria.* So Paul could mean, "I kneel before the father, the source of fatherhood." It could also again emphasize the oneness of lineage both Jews and Gentiles have together, that being of "Abraham's seed" is not nearly so crucial as being a child of God.

Study 7. Unity and Uniqueness. Ephesians 4:1-16.
Purpose: To see the place of unity and of unique gifts in the body of Christ.
Question 6. In *The Message of Ephesians,* John Stott writes, "To *maintain* the church's unity must mean to maintain it visibly. Here is an apostolic exhortation to us to preserve in actual concrete relationships of love . . . that unity which God has created and which neither man nor demon can destroy" (p. 152).
Question 7. The explanation is included here to avoid confusion about a very obscure passage. If members still have questions, ask if they could be discussed after the study. For now, focus on what we can draw out from these verses—Christ can and does give his people unique gifts.
Question 8. Certainly other gifts besides those in Ephesians 4 could be mentioned. But in general be careful that your whole discussion is not taken up on this point. How do you know you have these gifts? How can you develop them? And so on. You may want to follow up on these issues at some other group meeting. But for the purposes of this study, don't stay too long on this topic.
Question 11. If pressed for time, this could be skipped.

Study 8. Something Old, Something New. Ephesians 4:17-32.
Purpose: To consider the purity of conduct and communication necessary for maintaining unity in the body of Christ.
Question 2. The passage essentially has two halves. Questions 2-6 cover verses 17-24. Questions 7-12 cover verses 25-32.
Question 5. The command to put off our old self (our life before Christ) when we have already been made new in Christ is parallel to the command

to maintain unity when we are already one (4:3-4). We are to visibly act on the spiritual reality of being new creatures in Christ by discarding our old ways of life.

Question 7. Don't get hung up on filling in the outline in detail or hassling exactly which piece goes where. The purpose of the question is to give people a handle on what could otherwise look like a string of disconnected instructions.

Study 9. Live in Love, Live in Light. Ephesians 5:1-21.

Purpose: To continue to examine what it means for us to live worthy of our calling.

Questions 5-6. Some confusion could arise in your group over verses 5-6. These verses may seem to imply that we are saved by works apart from faith. In 5:3-4 Paul is speaking of individual acts which should be avoided. In verse 5 he switches from individual acts to the whole person, condemning a complete way of life, an entire orientation away from God's will. He spoke of such people previously in 2:1-3 and 4:17-19. The "immoral, impure or greedy person" is not condemned for isolated sinful acts but for his or her *lifestyle.*

Why would Paul raise such an issue if he is addressing Christians primarily? He was probably combating the Gnostic belief, quite prevalent then, that sins were irrelevant to one's spiritual state. No doubt many of his readers were influenced by such thinking. So he emphasizes, "Let no one deceive you." Obviously, an idolater is one whose life is not ruled by God but by some other passion. By definition, then, one whose lifestyle is idolatrous is cut off from God and subject to his wrath. There will be no need to go into this issue, of course, if it does not come up or your group is not troubled by it.

Question 10. Don't be distracted by preconceived ideas of what it means to be "filled with the Spirit." Focus the group's attention on what Paul says it means.

Question 13. Bring hymnbooks or songsheets with you to the study for the group to use. Or sing songs you all know by heart. If you have a guitarist in the group or a piano at hand, use these. If your group isn't made up of singers, then do as Paul suggests and "speak to one another with psalms, hymns and spiritual songs."

Study 10. Wives and Husbands. Ephesians 5:21-33.

Purpose: To consider how the relationship between Christ and the church can be a model for wives and husbands.

Hang onto your hats; there's a good chance this will be your most controversial study. But don't be afraid of controversy itself or of strong differences of opinion. Try to present an atmosphere of openness and willingness to hear all sides. However, don't be afraid to ask people to root their contentions in the passage. Your purpose is to see what Paul says here and not to bring in a myriad of outside resources and opinions. You may want to remind everyone before you start to stick to the passage!

Questions 5, 9, 12. We suggest that you make it clear to the group when a question is addressed to women and when it is addressed to men. Do not allow one sex to speak for or to evaluate the other. This is consistent with the fact that Paul addresses husbands and wives separately.

Note that verses 22-24 are instructions *to wives* in how they are to conduct themselves in marriage. They are not instructions to husbands on how they are to make their wives behave or on what they have a right to expect as husbands. Likewise verses 25-30 are instructions *to husbands* in how they are to conduct themselves in marriage. They are not instructions to wives on how they are to make their husbands behave or on what they have a right to expect as wives. Paul emphasizes the responsibilities of each and makes no comment on the rights of either. Thus we hope that in questions 5, 9 and 12 men do not respond if women were addressed or vice versa. The intent is for both to consider for themselves what their responsibilities are and how to respond.

Paul's instructions for both husbands and wives are given in the context of mutual submission (5:21), though Paul sees this acted out in different ways. Submission in either case, however, is counting others better than yourself. Paul calls on both husbands and wives to do this—husbands especially submitting to their wives by loving them and sacrificing whatever is necessary to meet their needs; wives especially submitting to their husbands by respecting them and honoring them as their head (see questions 11-12).

Question 11. In verse 33 Paul summarizes the different responsibilities of each spouse. Perhaps the reason for the difference is that while all human beings need both love and respect, women tend to feel more need for love, and men tend to feel more need for respect. Likewise it is often easier for women to give love and for men to give respect. So Paul focuses on the tougher assignment for each and on giving what the other needs most.

Study 11. Children, Parents, Slaves, Masters. Ephesians 6:1-9.

Purpose: To discover how Paul's discussion of parents and children and masters and slaves contributes to his theme of glorifying God through our unity.

Question 1. If people have trouble getting started, you could suggest one-word answers. "Stormy? Loving? Nonexistent? Casual? Close? Stiff? Open?" Allow a few minutes for all to speak who wish to.

Question 2. This study opens with a question giving an overview of the whole passage and closes with a question that reviews it (#14). Don't get into a lot of detail here since that is coming later. Look for general comments and observations.

Question 3. Some commentators see the promise of verse 3 as general rather than particular, applying to a family or family line or society as a whole rather than to an individual.

Question 4. Be ready for and open to negative answers. If they come, don't try to preach your position. Allow the group to struggle with the issues.

Question 5. If question 4 generates controversy, question 5 could bring things back together. Encourage the group to be concrete in how they will obey and honor their parents—if only in small ways.

Question 8. If there are parents, be sure you don't just cover the second half of verse 4 but the first half as well.

Study 12. Prayer Wars. Ephesians 6:10-24.

Purpose: To grasp how the ultimate battle is fought and how it can be won.

Question 1. There may be some in your group who do not believe in a personal devil. Allow them to express their views without getting into a big discussion of whether or not they are right. As the study moves on, Paul's position should become plain.

Question 2. See, for example, 1:3, 21; 2:2, 6 and 3:10. (This and question 8 ask you to look over the whole book of Ephesians. This can help tie the book together while touching on various points in 6:10-24.)

Question 5. Ephesians 3:1 and 4:1 also indicate his imprisonment.

Don't feel obligated to cover every piece of armor. It's more important to get the general idea of how we are prepared.

Question 7. If the group has trouble, suggest they look to Ephesians 6:18-20 for a response.

After the study. Ask each member to reread all of Ephesians in preparation for the last study which will review the whole letter.

Study 13. Looking Over the Letter Again. Ephesians 1—6.

Purpose: To review the whole letter, looking for its main themes and the main application Ephesians has for us.

Question 1. The words "in Christ" or "in him" are strewn throughout the letter. (For example, 1:3, 9, 11, 12; 2:6, 7, 10, 13, 21, 22; 3:6, 11, 12, 21 and so on.) They provide a wealth of material on the many facets of our union with Christ. You might ask several people in the group to look at one chapter each and then to report to the rest what they find.

Question 4. Ephesians 1:22-23 and 3:10-11 are mentioned only to give focus

to the discussion. Don't limit your discussion to these. Consider the thrust of
the letter and other passages which enrich our understanding of the church.

Questions 5-6. You may want to skip or abbreviate your discussion of these
questions if the answers to question 4 concentrate on the issue of unity
among believers. Perhaps you could ask instead, "Does anyone have anything
to add about unity in the body of Christ?" Be sure application of Paul's
teaching on unity is discussed.

Andrew T. Le Peau is managing editor of InterVarsity Press and the author of Paths of Leadership.
He and Phyllis J. Le Peau have combined to write several Bible study guides, including One Plus
One Equals One.